Gruts

IVOR CUTLER
GRUTS
with drawings by
MARTIN HONEYSETT

METHUEN

First published in Great Britain in 1962
by Museum Press Limited
This paperback edition first published in 1986
by Methuen London Ltd
11 New Fetter Lane, London EC4P 4EE

Made and printed in Great Britain

ISBN 0 413 40810 8

To Jack and Polly.

To my brain for composing the contents of this volume.

To my eyes which kindly read the proofs, and to all the other bits of my body, like my feet and my lungs, which helped too, though not as much as n:y eyes or my brain, of course.

Preface

I feel that a few incidents from my early childhood would help readers to understand the contents a little better. Some persons will prefer to read the contents first and leave the preface to the end. I do not know that I should not prefer to do the same myself, but I was faced with the difficulty of placing the preface at the back of the book, or perhaps two-thirds of the way through. This, I knew, would have been construed as 'interesting' or eccentric, so I decided to leave the preface at the beginning, and the time of its reading to the discretion of the reader.

Contents

Letter from a Grannie

'You? You know as much about ditch-digging as my granny!'

'Dear Sir,

'I heard your remark on the wireless, and I am writing in to tell you about myself. I am a grandmother with 81 grandchildren and I have been a ditch-digger all my life. You have only to ask the local authorities in the counties of Berkshire, Lincolnshire, Leicester and Peebles about 'Old Granny.' You will of course have to ask the department of roads, and they will furnish you with a full account of the work I have done with them.

'In my lifetime, I have dug something like 401,700 miles of ditches, and by this figure, I mean double-ditching. If you do not know what double-ditching is, it means "digging a ditch on both sides of the road so that you have two ditches". This is called "double-ditching".

'My husband was not able to become a ditcher because of the condition of his weak chest. He only attained the status of an asp-holder. None of our 13 children wanted to become ditch-diggers. They left home, and my husband and I went up and down the country digging ditches. At least, me digging ditches, and he holding the asp.

'A lot of fun is poked at grandmothers for being unable to do real, hard jobs, and I have written you this letter merely to show what a determined woman can do, confronted with the opportunity and the responsibility.

'Yours sincerely,
'Grandmother of 81.

'P.S. I am enclosing 2 sets of handprints. One set is of my own hands, and the other set is of my husband's hands, holding the asp.'

The Shchi

Legato

Look! The Shchi. The friendly little insect. It goes shchi-ing the whole day long. Look! The Shchi. The terrible terrible insect. It goes shchi-ing the world its song. Shchi! Shchi! Shchi! It goes shchi-ing the world its song. Shchi! Shchi! Shchi! It goes shchi-ing the world a-long. In the dawn, it goes shchi-ing its little song.

The Distant Pain

'Oh! Oh! Doctor. Oh! Doctor. I'm so glad you've come.'

'Why? What's the trouble, man?'

'Oh! Doctor. Oh! I've such a pain.'

'A pain? Where's your pain?'

'Oh! Over there in the corner.'

'I'm a busy man. I've no time for your nonsense. What do you mean?'

'Oh doctor. It's a bit difficult to explain. Sit down and I'll tell you. Last night when I went to sleep; when I go to sleep I dream.'

'Well, of course, everybody dreams.'

'I – I always leave my body when I dream. I leave my body in the bed and go elsewhere.'

'Of course.'

'And I was over there at the other side of the room, after I'd finished what I was doing in my dream and I was just about to come back to myself when suddenly a big fellow ran up to me with a loftsman's mallet and hit me right in the sconce – knocked me flat. Oo – a terrific – ff! Oh oh oh! When I think of it – a terrific crack – knocked me flat to the ground.'

'How unfortunate!'

'It was. There was I lying unconscious at the other side of the room and here was my body over on the bed.'

'Yes.'

'Well, when I woke up in the morning, and naturally I couldn't get back into myself, when I woke up in the morning, there was me over there unconscious. My body had gone, but the pain was still there. Oh doctor. It's such a pain. I wish you could cure it for me!'

'Ah! This presents some difficulty, you understand.'

'Couldn't you – couldn't you bring the pain over to my body and put it on to my head?'

'Well – I'll have a try if you like. Just you tell me when I touch it, will you.

.14.   Here, did you say?'

'No. Further over, by the cupboard. That's right. Further down. It's on the floor – Oh! Oh ho! Oh ho ho! Don't! Don't take it! – Oh! – Oh, doctor. That was it.'

'Now I'll just approach it again to locate it exactly.'

'Oh oh! Oh! Oh!'

'Now if I can get my hand under – '

'Ah! Aha! Oh!'

'It's right down on the ground. I can't get my hand underneath it. Mhm! We're snookered. Em! Let me think. There must be another way. – Ah! Tell me. I don't know if this'll work, but we can try it. Have you any – eh – meat in the house?'

'Oh no! No meat in the house.'

'Or fish?'

'No. Nothing like that. I've got an egg?'

'An egg? What kind of egg?'

'A hen's egg, of course.'

'All right, bring it in to me.'

'All right, hoo! Oh doctor, would you go and get it for me. It's outside in the egg-safe.'

'Here it is. Now I'm going to put the egg over here in the corner, exactly where the pain is. This may hurt a little, but it shouldn't be overwhelming.'

'Oh! Oh oh oh! Take it easy. Oh! Oh!'

'Right. There she is. Right on the pain. Now. Let's open my bag. Here you are. A cocaine spray. I'm going to freeze the pain into the egg. Ff! Ff! Ff! Ff! Ff! Ff! That's it from all sides. Give it a moment or two. Now I'm lifting it. Can you feel it changing direction?'

'Yes! It's over by the window now, the pain.'

'I'll bring it over to you. Shut your eyes, and see if you can locate it.'

'It's up by the light; it's on the floor; beside the bed; it's beside me.'

'Open your eyes.'

'Gosh, doctor, the pain's right in the egg! And I can barely feel it.'

'I'll leave you a little embrocation and here's a piece of red flannel. Now
listen! Embrocate it after two hours and it'll be gone by the morn.'

'Oh. Thank you, doctor, thank you. – There's just one point – eh – when
the pain goes, can I eat the egg?'

'You're a bit of a masochist, aren't you?'

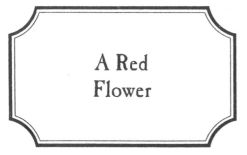

A Red Flower

'Good morning, madam.'

'Good morning. I wish to buy a red flower.'

'Certainly, madam. Is there any particular variety of flower you had in mind?'

'I wish to buy a red flower.'

'Certainly, madam. A large red flower, or a small one?'

'Size is a matter of indifference to me, just so it is a red flower.'

'Certainly, madam. A hyacinth, a crocus, or a daffodil, or perhaps one of
those charming lobelias, or we have narcissus, old man's beard and dandelion,
and coltsfoot too, of course.'

'I don't really mind, just so it is a red flower.'

'Certainly, madam. Pray be seated. Our Miss Jones will attend you. Miss
Jones, madam wishes to purchase a red flower.'

'Madam.'

'I should like a red flower.'

'Certainly, madam. Any particular variety?'

'Yes, red.'

'Ah! A large or small flower, madam?'

'Size is a matter of indifference to me. Just so it is red.'

'Yes, madam. Would this white hyacinth do?'

'Yes, indeed. It would do excellently well.'

'Will you take it, or shall I send it?'

'Would you please send it.'

'Certainly, madam. Any particular address?'

'No. No particular address. Just be sure to send it, and thank you. Good morning!'

'Good morning, madam.'

The Berserk Leg

'Help! Help! Help help! Help!'

'What's the trouble? What's the trouble? What's wrong?'

'My leg has gone berserk.'

'Goodness gracious what do you mean?'

'It's running down the street, kicking people.'

'Your leg? Why don't you run after it, and catch it?'

'How can I? – How can I run after it and catch it when I've only one leg left? If I hopped along, people would come and help me and I couldn't stand that kind of thing.'

'Where is it now?'

'I don't know. It ran away down the street, then it turned left and went round the corner – I suppose it's kicking people round there. Look at all the people standing about, rubbing themselves.'

'Yes. I'd noticed them. They seemed to be, how shall we say, lacking in dignity.'

'They don't know whose leg's been kicking them. A good thing they don't realize it's mine.'

'How are you going to recover it?'

'Oh, I don't know. I'll just wait till it gets tired and comes back.'

'You mean – it's done this kind of thing before?'

'Oh, yes. It does it every day, when we go out.'

'Haven't you seen a doctor about it?'

'Of course. I see a doctor every day, whenever I get my leg back.'

'And what does the doctor say? Doesn't he get fed up with you calling every day?'

'Oho yes. He does. Every time he sees me he gets terribly angry. His face goes all red and he says "Get out! I don't want to see you, you and your berserk leg." You see, he's never seen my leg going berserk and he thinks I'm just pulling his – eh, he thinks I'm just, eh, being funny with him.'

'You've no way of convincing him.'

'No. When my leg comes back and joins on there's nothing to indicate that it's been berserk.'

'Tell me, why does your leg keep going berserk?'

'Oh, I think it's just having a last fling.'

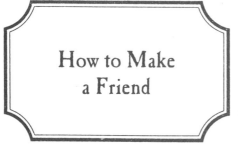

How to Make a Friend

Do you find it difficult to make friends?

I am. At least I was, until I discovered how to do it.

First of all, take a large bucket of whitewash, then stand by the window and look out. When you see someone approaching whom you would like to know, wait until he is directly below, then empty the bucket over his head.

He will stop, and look up, and shout unspeakable language at you. You will then reply, 'Do come upstairs and clean yourself up' and throw him down the key.

He will pick up the key and enter your home, tramping whitewash into the carpet all the way up.

You will say, 'Come. Have a bath,' light the geyser and start running the water. He will take his clothes off, and as he is taking them off say, 'Ah! you have a hole in your undervest. Let me mend it while you are having your bath.' He will say, 'Thank you. I am very grateful for this.'

While he is in the bath, sit there talking to him, darning his vest. It doesn't matter what kind of thread you use, it is the deed which is important. I myself use cobbler's thread, because when he wears the vest and feels the cobbler's thread against his skin, it is a constant reminder to him of our friendship and

he thinks, 'I must phone this man again.'

When he is dry, hand him your best red silk dressing-gown, with the dragons; then he can take his clothes, put them into the bath-water and wash them, then hang them out of the window to dry.

Say to him, 'Come and sit with me and talk to me by the window while they are drying.' Then you talk, enjoying one another's conversation.

By this time the clothes are dry. Fetch them in and he will don them, thanking you for the darn on his vest.

As it is now lunch, you offer him a share of your dinner.

After dinner he says, 'Well, I must really go now,' and as you go downstairs he notices with alarm the whitewash on the carpet and says, 'Goodness! Look what I have done to your carpet.' And you say, 'No, no! I only rent a room here. It is the landlord's carpet.' Then he says, 'We cannot let you get into bad odour with the landlord. Let us together clean this carpet.' So you clean the carpet, and this makes you even closer friends.

When you have cleaned the carpet, he says, 'Well, I must really go now, but I shall come and see you again tomorrow, and we shall have another long talk.'

You have made a friend.

When he has gone, go back to the window with another bucket of whitewash, where you can stand, or sit, as is your wont, ready to make another friend.

The Footkerchief

'Son, wipe your knees!'

'I can't, Mammy. I've lost my footkerchief.'

'Here. Use mine. Now, wipe your knees!'

These words halted me as I walked by the disused factory wall. Here was someone I could understand. I strode over and shouted, 'Show me your footkerchief!'

She showed me. With a howl of joy I took her into my arms and pressed her close to me, laughing wildly all the time. 'Footkerchief! Footkerchief!' I mumbled into her ear.

I was interrupted by a large, jolly man, who pulled us apart without ceremony and said, 'Are you embracing my wife?' Then with a tremendous, jolly laugh, he flung me to the ground, and planted one foot on my chest.

'Let me up! Let me rise!' I shouted.

'No, no, no, ha-ha-ha, no, no!' he laughed. 'Just you stay down there.'

I lifted his trouser leg, the one that was on his chest, pulled his black sock down, and scratched – you know that little hollow, under the ankle bone – the one where you sometimes see little veins. But he paid me no heed. Thick-skinned, I suppose. He was talking about shopping, how he'd done a lot of shopping. And he went through each item, and all the bargains he'd made. The child meantime was standing facing the wall.

I prised myself from under the jolly man's foot, ran over to the woman, and once again seized her in my embrace, whispering, 'Footkerchief! Footker-chief.' My hand, exploring the back of her head, caught in the hair at the nape of her neck, but alas, not for long. The big jovial man sundered us, and threw me to the ground, laughing furiously. This time, instead of putting one foot on me, he put both feet – one on my chest and one on my stomach, and as he went on telling his wife about his purchases, he would jump after each purchase,

like – eh – 'I bought a big bunch of bananas.' Jump! 'I bought a pound of apples.' Jump! 'I bought three dozen oranges.' Jump! And so on.

'Stop it! Stop it!' I screamed.

'Shut up!' he screamed back. Jump! 'I bought a loaf of bread.' Jump!

The woman, whom I was beginning to suspect was his wife, said, "Enough's enough,' and they walked away.

I scrambled to my feet. The woman turned her head, and with a glorious smile suffusing her face, threw me her wig.

The Greasy Button

'Hello, Hamish!'

'Hello, Terence. What have you got there?'

'A button.'

'Let me see it. Oh! It's greasy. Where did you get it from?'

'I pulled it off my jacket.'

'How did it get all greasy?'

'I've been oiling my scooter.'

'What with?'

'Lard.'

'That's what makes it greasy?'

'Yes.'

'Do you think it's worth anything?'

'I don't really know. I just don't know the market value of a button.'

'Well, I suppose you could take it along to a button-valuer.'

'Don't be silly! There's no such thing as a button-valuer.'

'Well, take it to a jeweller then. He'll value it for you. There's one in the High Street.'

'All right. Come on. Here we are – Theseus Spinesnapper, Jeweller.'

'Good morning.'

'Good morning. We've brought you this to value.'

'It's a button.'

'Yes, I know.'

'It's greasy.'

'Yes, I know.'

'Well, I should say it's worth — eh, a penny.'

'A penny? Is that all? That's lard on it.'

'Oh well, a penny farthing then.'

'Oh, a penny farthing's not much use. You see we want to share it between the two of us.'

'All right. Look. Nobody's going to call me a mean man. I'll give you three ha'pence for it.'

'That seems fair enough.'

'And, of course, there's five shillings for the valuation. So if you give me four and tenpence ha'penny we'll call it quits. All right?'

'All right, here's the four and tenpence ha'penny. — Come on, Hamish, let's go and find a sweetie shop and buy nothing.'

The Ouch-Stopit-Merriman String Quartet

'Hey! The Ouch-Stopit-Merriman String Quartet will be on in a minute.

Switch on the wireless.'

'Good evening, lazies and gentlemen. This is station DRAB. We present, for your ineffable entertainment, The Ouch-Stopit-Merriman String Quartet! Before the quartet commences, here is an announcement: Do you buy "Absolute Rubbish"? Then when this programme is over, go back to the shop from which you bought it – and buy some more. You deserve it. "Absolute Rubbish" – the product which makes all your friends feel superior. Now the quartet.'

'Zz zz zz zz zz zz zz zz.'

'Turn that damn thing off. What an impertinence.'

'Station DRAB. Dear Sirs, I listened this evening to the Ouch-Stopit-Merriman String Quartet. All I heard was "Zz zz." Do you call this music? I am accustomed to listening to primitive noises with satisfaction, but really!

'Yours indignantly, Ivor Cutler.'

'Dear Mr Cutler, I can only assume that you wrote in ignorance of the function of the Ouch-Stopit-Merriman String Quartet. They do not play *on* string, they play *with* it. Actually, they no longer play with string. As their proficiency increased, rope was substituted, and last night they filled our concert-studio with a huge cats-crazle, using a hawser. The noise you heard, "zz zz", was the sound made by one piece of hawser rubbing against another piece of hawser.

'Yours faithfully, Jeremiah Twillfeeler,
Public Relations Officer, Station DRAB.'

The Hoorgi House

I visited the Hoorgi House. The walls were green and it was crowded. The mechanical men stood behind the counter with large smiles. You nodded, and they dropped something on your plate, like a gherkin or a chop or a red radish.

I filled my plate and sat with twenty people at a round table. Whilst eating, I watched the servers. Not a soul asked the gravy man for gravy and his smile was bitter. I determined to sweeten his smile. The following day I entered the Hoorgi House, lifted a deep plate and made straight for the gravy man. 'Fill my plate with gravy, gravy man,' I smiled. His ladle entered the great bin of gravy strapped to his shoulders, and with incredible rapidity he filled my plate with the rich brown fluid. 'Thank you,' I said, but he kept on spooning gravy and as I turned to find my place at the table he came after me, spooning gravy furiously. As he came from behind the counter, I noticed that he had no feet. In their place were two little wheels, which bore him along.

Ignoring him, I sat at the round table and started drinking my gravy; but I was hampered in this by the gravy man, who stood beside me, pouring ladles full of gravy over my head and shoulders. I was smothered, yet I did not dare to rise from my place and call attention to myself. The Hoorgi House is exclusive. Suddenly, the gravy man stopped. His bin was empty. He returned to the counter. I sighed hysterically and sat back, wiping myself unobtrusively with a napkin. But the gravy man is coming back with a fresh bin!

Smartly, I ran to the door, and as I paid my cheque at the exit, he caught up with me and started working his ladle. I left the restaurant, the gravy man just behind me, and we rushed down the street till we reached my house, where I slipped in and placed the street door between us.

The letter-box opened and gravy poured in. 'Stop!' I bellowed through the letter-box. 'Why do you do this to *me*?' The gravy came to a stop. His face came to the letter-box and snarled, 'You are the man who demanded a foot

salad last week!' Of course! The wheels! 'So it was *your* feet?' 'Yes! My feet.'
I pushed a yardstick and a handsaw through the letter-box. 'Cut what you
need,' I shouted, acting on a generous impulse. 'A waiter needs a couple of
good feet!'

The Windpipe

'I say, there's old McDonald over there.'
'So it is. Do you know him?'
'I'll say I know him, the old wind-pipe.'
'Windpipe? You mean windbag, don't you?'
'No – no. I mean windpipe.'
'Tell me what you mean.'

'This goes back eighty years. I was quite young. McDonald and I stayed in
the same street. We played together.'

'Yes, well how is he a windpipe?'

'We used to play this game. There was a big stony field close by and
McDonald and I used to take our spades that we brought back from the
seaside and dig a hole.'

'Yes, go on.'

'We wanted to keep a prisoner down the hole. We would dig the hole six
feet deep and three – no four and a half or five feet in diameter. I used to think
three feet then but I was younger. Down six feet, then along about nine or
eleven, then hollow it out into a great chamber. Fit it up with carpets, cushions
and electric light. Of course it's pretty inconceivable now, but then it was very
real.'

'Yes. Well, go on.'

'We dug down the six feet. Mind you, we were only four: I was nearly five
at the time actually, and it was difficult going, through hard-packed soil. It was
used as a football field at the week-ends. Then we dug along and smoothed the
walls with water brought down in an old cucumber tin. We dug the eleven feet,
as it was soft going, and removed the soil in an old bottomless bucket to the
surface, where we dispersed it around the field. Then we hollowed out the

chamber and stole carpets and cushions from our homes. For electricity we
used an old accumulator from my father's car. It gave us thirty-five watts, I
remember. Then we waited for a victim. It would be Peggy or Millie. Peggy
was too mature, she was six; Millie was four. We tried to inveigle her down.
McDonald, he was always a good talker, as you know, he said, "Come on
down, Millie," and Millie said, "No, I'm not coming down with you two
boys." She was a little afraid of us, I think. McDonald said, "Come on,
Millie, I want to show you something." She looked as though she'd heard that
one before, but she came anyway. You fell down the six feet, more or less, and
the footballers used to create about this great hole in the ground because the
ball used to fall in all the time. We went down and along the passage into the
room. Millie gasped when she saw it lit up and said, "Are you not afraid?"
"No," said McDonald, "I'm not afraid. Look!" And he bent his knee and
jumped right through the roof so that his head stuck out of the ground.
"Look," he said, "I'm a windpipe." '

The Judge's Parcel

'Hello, Judge!'

'Hello, Ivor!'

'What you got there, Judge?'

'In my parcel?'

'What've you got in your parcel, Judge?'

'Justice, Ivor. Justice.'

'Let me see it.'

'Not out in the street here. I'll show you if you can take me somewhere where I can show you it.'

'It's only three-quarters of a mile along the road to the railway station. There's a very quiet waiting-room, the men's waiting-room. All the men go to the *general* waiting-room to look at women.'

'Very well.'

When we reached the waiting-room the judge set the parcel on the table.

'Hurry, Judge. Open it.'

'Patience, Ivor. These knots are a bit tricky and I don't want to damage the string. Now then. Look! Justice!'

It was a large bottle, a two-gallon bottle, with a narrow pourer and a tiny cup hanging from the handle.

'Is this Justice?'

'Yes. This is Justice.'

'How does it work?'

'You dispense it through the pourer into the cuplet and then before you go into the court to judge people you quaff it.'

'And does it always make you give the right decision?'

'Oh yes. This is one hundred per cent Justice. No filler in this.'

I went down on my knees before the judge and clasped his striped trousers.

'Judge!' I looked up into his face. 'Judge! Judge me!'

His face became lined and grim. 'I've had a hard day, Ivor,' he said.

He took the bottle, and through the narrow pourer – poured a little Justice
into the cup, and he handed it to me.

'Here, Ivor. Judge yourself.'

Fish Fright

'Here! Here! Can you give me something for fish fright?'

'I'll beg your pardon?'

'Can you give me something for fish fright?'

'I'm sorry. I don't understand what you mean.'

'Look! My girl's sitting out there on my motor-bike. She's suffering from fish fright. Can you give me something for fish fright?'

'Well! I've never heard of fish fright.'

'Oh! What a dope! We've just come down from Derwentwater. She caught fish fright there, from a carp.'

'I'm terribly sorry. I've never heard of the disease. Perhaps you'd like to bring her in and I'll have a look at her and see if I can prescribe something for her, but of course, it's not really my business to prescribe; you ought to see a doctor.'

'Oh! It just came on all of a sudden. She suddenly told me to stop, and you were open.'

'Come in here. Here you are, sit her down by the counter – Is *this* your girl-friend?'

'Of course, it's my girl-friend. I've just brought her in, haven't I?'

'But – but she looks – she looks just like a fish – like a carp.'

'Well of course she looks like a carp. She's got fish fright, hasn't she?'

'Then – who's that sitting out there on the pillion of your motor-bike?'

'Oh! that's my Auntie Margaret.'

'And hasn't she got fish fright?'

'No. She was looking the other way.'

The Ageing Butterfly

'Hello, you beautiful thing.'

'Hello.'

'I've never seen anyone so beautiful as you in all my life.'

'I don't think you ought to talk like that to me. I'm a maiden.'

'And me?'

'You're a married man with eleven children.'

'That doesn't mean to say that I'm blind to beauty.'

'I dare to say, but a married man with eleven children doesn't come up to a girl in the street and tell her she's beautiful.'

'Why not?'

'You're supposed to be settled down.'

'Look. In spite of my encumbrances, I've still an eye for beauty, and whenever I see beauty, I just can't help myself, I have to talk to it. I was in the British Museum the other day at the reproduction counter. Suddenly my eye lit on a photograph, a coloured photograph, of a Chinese pot, late seventeenth century – and I fell in love with it. And I took it out of the rack and I gave the woman a sixpence and she put it in a paper bag and I looked at it and I kissed it because it was so beautiful.'

'Well, why don't you go back to the British Museum and buy yourself another photograph and kiss it. I don't like being compared with a pot.'

'Oh, you're both beautiful. This was a beautiful pot and you're a beautiful girl.'

'Well, I still don't like it. It's inanimate – and I'm animate.'

'You don't look very animate, crouching all hunched up at the end of the public bench. As a matter of fact, you look half-dead to me.'

'Naturally I look half-dead to you, with your eleven children and your wife all standing round us and glaring at us in a ring with their teeth bare.'

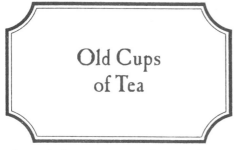

Old Cups of Tea

'Old cups of tea! Here, mister, would you like to buy an old cup of tea?'

'Er, yes, perhaps; let me have a look at them. All poured out I see. How much are they?'

'Well, there's um, there's three-ha'penny cups of tea and penny cups of tea, and ha'penny cups of tea and some cups of tea are free.'

'Oh. Could I have a free cup of tea?'

'If you want to.'

'*You're* not very encouraging. *Can* I have a free cup of tea?'

'All right. One of those!'

'Tsppah! urrgh! Oh it's horrible! Urragh!'

'You see. I wasn't very keen for you to have one.'

'Ugh my goodness I feel sick. You must have had that tea for months.'

'Yes, we've had it since June.'

'Ugh goodness gracious. I think I'd better have one of the more expensive ones. What's the difference between the ha'penny and the penny and so on?'

'Well, it depends, it – it's the freshness of it. You see, we buy. There's a lot of cafés round here, you see. – Well, when they've poured out cups of tea they don't use we buy them from them, and if you can get a cup of tea that's still a little warm we're going to charge you a penny-ha'penny for that; and if it's gone cold but it's fresh, then we charge you a penny and so on, right down to the free cups of tea. We don't mind giving people free cups of tea because it gives them such a bad taste in their mouths that they're only too pleased to buy one of the better ones.

'Oh, here's some tea coming now – here's a three-ha'penny cup coming. Just a minute till I dip my finger in; yes, it's still warm. Would you like one?'

'Yes, I'll – try anything to get this taste out.'

'Just a minute till I stir it. You like your tea sweet, don't you?'

.38.   'Yes, I like it sweet.'

'I'll stir it with the wee stick. There now, that'll be three-ha'pence.'

'Ah, this is a bit better, but it's nearly stone cold.'

'Well, I know; I mean, if you want to buy a proper retail-price cup of tea then you're going to have to pay the full price, aren't you? You should be grateful to get it for this price. We don't cater for toffs, you know. We just cater for very poor people, likes of myself. You actually look a bit too rich to be coming patronizing this stall. I think you'd better go away and buy yourself a proper cup of tea.'

'I certainly shall. I didn't realize that this stall was for poor people. I'm going to go away and get a proper cup of tea and pay the full price, and enjoy it.'

'That's right. Go away and enjoy your tea and while you're enjoying your tea, you think of all the people that come into my stall, buying, that can't afford more than a ha'penny cup of tea where the milk's all sour and there's no sugar in it. And the free cups of tea. Just think of the people who can't afford anything but the free cups of tea and then be grateful.'

'I'm going to do better than that. I'm going to think about all the people who can't even afford to buy *free* cups of tea. They're the lucky ones.'

The Human Awl

'Come on, son, we're going to the circus,' said my mother, a large, grim-lipped woman.

I donned my shiny black boots and hat and followed her, my heart leaping with excitement. Our seats were well back. I gauged the circumference of the ring to be about four hundred and seventy feet.

After an hour of the usual, a drum rolled and the manager ran out. 'Friends!' he called. This evoked a hostile reaction. One old man, a parish councillor, unlaced his boot and threw it at him. We are rugged and independent in our part of the country. 'You now will see the Human Awl,' he continued, impervious to our rugged independence. 'This man will pierce the sole of a six-foot boot, thus enabling it to be sewn to the upper.' Then he ran out of the ring. A large gang of assistants ran in with a six-foot upper, which they placed on the perimeter, toe upmost. A second gang of assistants ran in with a six-foot sole, six inches thick, which they propped against the upper. On the sole were little splashes of whitewash, to indicate the position of the holes.

The Human Awl stalked in and stood at the centre of the arena. He must have weighed twenty stone and was dressed in a navy-blue serge suit, double-breasted, which was so large that the front buttons had been resewn on his hip. From his left pocket he took a tenpenny nail and from the right a piece of string. He tied the nail-head at the middle of the string, then, holding the nail point upwards on his head, secured it with string to his ears.

He returned to the perimeter opposite the boot, then ran as fast as he could to the centre, took off and sailed through the air to stick, head first, into the big sole. He stuck there, quivering, horizontal, for a few seconds, then disengaged himself, pressing hard against the sole with his elbows and knees. Once more he returned to the perimeter, blew his nose, and took off, landing square on a whitewash splash.

After he had pierced a dozen or so holes, I became concerned for his head,
and rising to my feet, shouted, 'Stop, mister! You'll do your head an injury!'
He stopped half-way along his run and came lumbering over, panting audibly,
to look up with an ineffably reassuring smile into my face. He removed the
string from his ears and held the nail up for me to see. 'Look, laddie,' he said,
'it's a rubber nail,' and he waggled it. 'It's an elevenpenny nail.' I buried my
face in my mother's fichu, sobbing with relief.

The Jamme-Beanabody Affair

'Oh! You handsome, handsome man!'
　'Ah hahahahaha! You don't really mean that!'
　'Yes, indeed I do.'
　'Well, you look pretty good as well.'
　'Really?'

'Oh, yes. So much so that I should like to make you a proposal.'

'What kind?'

'A marriage proposal.'

'Go on then. Make it.'

'Will you marry me?'

'Yes, I will. Come on. I know a place where we can get married. – Here!'

'But this is a grocer's shop!'

'I know, but this grocer marries people in his spare time.'

　'Excuse me, have you time to marry us?'

　'I'll be with you in just a minute. That's fourteen and a halfpenny. Call it
fourteen shillings.'

　'Thank you.'

　'Now then, you want to get married?'

　'Yes.'

　'Right, now, what is your name?'

　'My name is James Jamme, double M, E.'

　'And *your* name?'

.42.   '*My* name is Persista Beanabody.'

'Persista Beanabody. Right. Now just repeat after me: 'I,' 'I,' 'I,' 'am', 'am,' 'am,' 'married,' 'married,' 'married,' 'There you are.'

'Thank you very much, Mr. Grocer.'

'Don't mention it. Any time.'

'I must go home and tell Mummy and Daddy that I'm married.'

'Yes, you do that, and I'll see you after lunch.'

'Oh, I – I've got to go back to the office this afternoon but I'll see you after six.'

'Aw – that's not much good to me, I – I'm going to a film tonight. It's a particularly good one, otherwise I'd have cancelled it. How about tomorrow?'

'Oh, tomorrow – that's Wednesday, I'm playing tennis. And – dear, Thursday I can't come either, Aunt Florrie's coming over. And Friday – Friday's the night that I wash my hair. How about Saturday?'

'Well, Saturday I'm playing cricket. Saturday evening any good to you?'

'Saturday eve . . . no, no, that's the whist drive.'

'Look, give me your number and I'll phone you sometime, O.K.?'

'O.K.'

The Man
with the
Trembly Nose

Slowly, with much feeling.

mf Who is looking over your shoulder

when you are standing reading a news-

paper? The man with the trembly

nose. The man with the trembly nose.

p Do not be embarrassed. Turn quietly a-

round and whisper in his ear,

ff "Stop reading my paper! Stop trembling your

nose!f You are driving me mad.

mf You are driving me mad."

The Dirty Dinner

'Oh! What's that on the dining-room table? Jim! Jim! Come here. What's that on the dining-room table?'

'That's a big pile of dirt, Mammy.'

'What's it doing on the dining-room table?'

'I shovelled it on.'

'Why? Don't you know we're having visitors tonight? The Smiths are coming.'

'Yes, Mammy, I know. But Daddy said, "I'd like to make the Smiths eat dirt." '

'Oh! You silly boy. He didn't mean that. Now, come on, get rid of it.'

'Aw, Mammy. It's took me a long time to put it on – '

'Get rid of it and – just a minute, change into your slippers before you climb on to the table – and not a sharp spade in case you dent the veneer. Watch now. I don't want dirt all over the carpet. What else is on the table besides the dirt?'

'Bill.'

'Bill? How long has he been there?'

'From the beginning, I suppose.'

'Let's have a look. Bill! Are you all right, Bill?'

'Yes, Mammy. I'm all right. I've drilled a wee hole in the table and I can breathe through and I can see the carpet too. I drilled a hole for an eye.'

'Oh my goodness. Just stay there, Bill, till Jim's got rid of the dirt. We don't want any on the carpet. And don't move in case any of the dirt goes through the holes.'

'All right, Mammy.'

'Now Jim. Come on. Get rid of some of this dirt.'

'O.K. Can I put the pail on the chair?'

'Yes. Just a minute! Just a minute! Let me put a bit of paper on it. Aw!

Didn't you wipe the bottom of the pail?'

'Oh, no, Mammy.'

'Give it here! There! Put it on the chair. Now watch. Careful son. That's enough. Just take the bucket and empty it out the window.'

'Empty it out the window, Mammy? There's people passing.'

'Son, we've got to get rid of this dirt in a hurry. Just empty it out the window. Be careful, that's all. Try and spread it in a wide arc, so that, you know, all of it won't fall on one person.'

'Ha ha ha ha ha! Mammy. There's one or two people looking up.'

'Aw crumbs. Come inside quick for goodness' sake. Bring that pail in with you. Here. Fill it again. Quickly. That's right. Now not so much this time. Throw it out the window. No! Not that window! This side window. No, no, scatter it. Aw crumbs. You fool. Quick. Come in. Come in, come in! Right. Fill it up again. Now out the other one. No no. The first window that you put it out. Watch your feet! Watch your feet! Oh don't get that dirt into the carpet. Wait a minute. I'll get a brush and shovel. Now, come on. Round. That's right. Work round it. There. Now throw it out in a wide arc. That's the way to do it. Is that the bell? Just a minute. I'll answer the door. Go on shovelling.'

'Hey, are you all right, Bill?'

'Yes, Jim. I'm all right.'

'What's it like with all the earth on top of you?'

'Lovely. Was Mammy very annoyed? I couldn't see her face.'

'Sh! Here's Mammy coming back. (*Whistles.*) Who was it, Mammy?'

'Nobody you know. Hurry up.'

(*Hums.*) 'Whsh!' (*Sings to 'da di da.'*)

'That's a good boy. I say, where's Bill?'

'Bill? What do you mean?'

'I thought he was on the table.'

'Ho no. That was only a joke, Mammy.'

'Where's the hole that he was breathing through?'

'Aw Mammy. Why don't you have a wee lie down? I'll finish off the table and polish it with beeswax. It'll be all ready in time for the Smiths.'

First Love

Now one evening I was walking down the street when I saw a little grey girl.

She looked very poor to me but someone told me afterwards she was very rich.

You couldn't tell from her clothes; they were so very simple. Had I been wise I would have seen that her simplicity cost her a fortune.

She smiled at me and I took a deep breath and walked on. And there she was, following me.

I turned to the left. I turned to the left again, and the left and the left. She kept following me – round the block. I went very fast until I was following her.

'Oho! You sonsy creature,' she says. 'What are you doing? What are you doing?' I didn't say anything at all. I just smiled at her very gravely. It was hardly a smile: it was more of a – a leer. She – she threw me a dissipated look and I blenched. I had never seen a look like that before ever in my life, and of course it captivated me.

Eventually I found my tongue. 'Come on,' I said. She fainted: right into my arms.

I lifted her: took her into the nearest tenement. We walked a flight; two flights; three flights of stairs. I laid her down on the step to recover, and lay down myself to recover too. She looked around. 'Where am I?' 'Oh, we're on the third floor of a tenement.' 'What's a tenement?' 'Well, flats. Key flats.' So we went on up. We came to the seventh, eighth, ninth, and when we came to the seven-hundred-and-twenty-fourth flight she drawled, 'You know, this is a long way. Where are you going?' And I answered, 'Oh, I live on the seven-hundred-and-twenty-eighth floor.' So we ran up the last four flights and I produced a flat key – remember – it was a key flat. I produced a key, twisted it into the door and the door sprang: open.

.48.   'Come in,' I said. She staggered dreamily in, through the hell into the living-room, lay down on the elegant sofa and kicked off her shoes over the end. I gasped. This was living. I took a cigar from my vest, lit it at a candle that I lit specially for the purpose, and started puffing away furiously, blowing as much smoke as I could into her face: directly, and indirectly too, through my big ears. Her eyes stared into mine, but only for a second or two. They began to smart. 'Stop blowing that damn cigar smoke at me,' she wept, 'who the devil do you think I am?' 'Who are you?' I rasped. 'Who are you?' 'Oh, you fool!' she moaned, 'you fool. You don't understand the first thing about me.' 'I do. I do I do,' I said. 'I understand the first thing about you. And the second thing, too.' 'Ah ha ha,' she laughed, 'you are a man.' 'Me?' I ran – I ran next door into the bedroom to the pier-glass and peered into it. Then I ran back to her. 'Yes, yes,' I gloated, 'I am a man.' She sat up suddenly on the sofa and looked about her. 'What am I doing here talking to you seven-hundred-and-twenty-eight floors up? I want to go home: Mother wants me.' 'Mother wants you!' I jeered. 'Mother wants you. Eleven times round the block. Mother wants you. Go to your mother. Where does she live?' 'On the ground floor.'

I picked her up and dropped her with contumely down the lift-shaft.

She went down rather quickly though she told me the following week that she'd had time to sing the whole of *Traviata* and the first eleven bars of *Trovatore*.

Needless to say, I never spoke to another woman in all my life.

Never: ever.

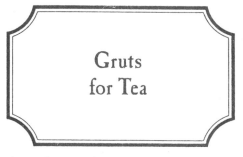

Gruts
for Tea

'Hello, Billy, teatime! Gruts for tea! –
Billy! Billy! Come on, son. Gruts for
tea! Fresh gruts!'

'Oh, I don't want gruts for tea,
Daddy.'

'What? I went out specially and got
them for you.'

'Aw, but Daddy, we had gruts yesterday.'

'Look, son, I walked seven miles to the High Wood to get you gruts. That's
fourteen miles in all, counting the journey back, and you don't want gruts? I
fried them for you. Fried gruts – mm – I fried them in butter.'

'I don't want them, Daddy. Daddy, we've had gruts for three years now. I'm
fed up with gruts. I don't want them any more. Daddy, can't we have
something else for tea?'

'Oh, son! Gruts! They're lovely.'

'Daddy, I don't want gruts any more. I hate gruts. I detest them. I have
them every day and they're always fried in butter. Can't you think of another
way of cooking gruts? There's hundreds of ways of cooking gruts: boil them or
bake them or stew them or braise them – but every day – fried gruts. "Billy,
come in for tea. Fried gruts. I've walked fourteen miles. Seven miles to the
High Wood and back." Three years of gruts. Look what it's done to me,
Daddy! Come here! Come here into the bedroom and look at ourselves in the
mirror, you and me. Now, look at that!'

'Yes. I see what you mean. Son, let's not waste these gruts. Tomorrow I'll
go to the High Wood and get something else.'

'Look, Daddy, you've been saying this for three years now. Every day we
have this same thing. I take you to the mirror and you say we'll have
something else for tea. What else is there in the High Wood besides gruts?'

'Well, there's leaves, bark, grass, and leaves. Gruts are really the best. You
must admit it.'

'Yes, Daddy, I admit it. Gruts are really the best, but I don't want them. I hate them. I detest them. In fact I'm going to take this panful of gruts and throw them out.'

'Oh, don't do that! Don't throw them out for goodness' sake! You'll poison the dog!'

Egg-Meat

'Mammy, do you want any errands?'

'Yes, son, go down to the ironmonger and buy me a pound of egg-meat.'

'Egg-meat? What's egg-meat?'

'Never you mind. Just go and buy it. Here's five shillings and I want the change.'

'All right. Mammy, can I have something?'

'Yes. Keep a penny and buy that.'

'Thanks. I'm away . . . Mammy, I'm back with the egg-meat.'

'Have you got the change?'

'Yes. The egg-meat was tenpence. Here's four and a penny.'

'Thank you. Now just you go out and play while I deal with the egg-meat.'

'What are you going to do with the egg-meat, Mammy?'

'Ha ha, you silly boy. I'm going to feed it to the eggs . . .'

'Mammy, what do you mean – feed it to the eggs; that doesn't make sense.'

'Eh, son, I've never told you this, but I've some eggs here – I keep them in a box.'

'Yes, Mammy, I know. We sometimes have an egg.'

'No, no, son – this is different eggs – and I feed them meat.'

'Mammy, why does the ironmonger sell egg-meat?'

'Well, somehow or other he could make it the best, and we just know, the people that buy it around here, where to buy it from, because he's the only one round here that has it. Ha ha! You couldn't go into the dairy and ask for a

pound of egg-meat. They'd look at you askance, wouldn't they?'

'Can I see the eggs?'

'Oh, well, I'm not very keen to show you the eggs: they should really be kept in the dark. You see, they've, eh – nocturnal habits.'

'Ah ha ha, Mammy, you use these big words. I'm proud of you. You use the biggest words. You use the biggest words of any woman in our street. I heard you talking to Mrs. Machinery, and, oh Mammy, these big words you used. Gosh and Mrs. Machinery's face wasn't half red.'

'That'll do, son. Now, the egg-meat. (*Sniffs.*) Smells fresh.'

'Mammy, is egg-meat *always* that colour?'

'No, not always. It's sometimes a bit more orangey, but this is the usual colour.'

'It's got a funny smell, hasn't it?'

'Yes. It's funny till you're used to it.'

'Oh Mammy, I love this. It's fun. Now show me how you feed it to the eggs.'

'All right. Come into the bedroom and pull the blinds.'

'But if I do that I'll not be able to see.'

'I know. You've got to feed it to them in the dark. Just a minute. I'll leave the door a wee bit open so that a little light comes in so that you don't tumble over things. Now, watch . . . there . . . did you see the way they grabbed it?'

'Ah yes. It was wonderful . . . Mammy, can I buy egg-meat for you every day?'

'Yes, son, every day. You're a big boy now. You can buy egg-meat for me . . . every day.'

The Tureen

'Hello, James.'

'Hello, Philip.'

'That's a fine tureen you have there.'

'Yes, isn't it? Seventeenth-century.'

'Bai Gad, it looks delicate.'

'It may look delicate, but it's not. Very strong.'

'M-hm! What are you doing walking along the street carrying a tureen, for?'

'We're having a business merger, and I'm taking this tureen along to the merger.'

'Oh. Tell me, what's in it?'

'Soup. Hot soup.'

'Hot soup, eh? What – what kind of hot soup?'

'Chicken soup.'

'Chicken soup? – that's my favourite soup.'

'I say, let me sniff it, will you?' (*Sniff.*)

'Look, I'm in a hurry. I'd like to get along to the dinner.'

'Oh, but chicken soup! How did you make it?'

'Well, I cooked it in tabasco sauce.'

'Aw – You know, don't you.'

'Of course I know. I've made it often enough.'

'I say. Do you know – what – tabasco sauce can do for your feet?'

'No. No. I don't know. What can it do for your feet?'

'Are your feet sore?'

'Of course my feet are sore walking along the street with this damn great tureen.'

'Just pop your feet into this chicken soup.'

'All right, but only for a minute. Here, let's set it down in the gutter.'

'Let me put my feet in too. My feet are killing me.'

'Oh, very well, there's enough room for two pairs of feet. There are 165 portions of soup in here.'

'Oh! La la! Ooh! Ho! Ahh! Marvellous! Ahh! Oh gosh! Heaven! heaven! Mm!'

'Yes. Jolly good.'

'I say. Why are you putting your feet in, in your shoes and socks?'

'Oh, if once I took my shoes and socks on, I should never get them off again, but I can feel it just the same. It gets in over the edges of the shoes, you know. You're right, but gad, it's pretty wonderful. Ah! I think that's about enough. I'd better be getting back to them. Here! Hand me the lid, will you. I'll see you another time. Sorry I can't stay. Good-bye!'

The
Handymen

'All ready, Sam?'
'Yes, Jim!'
'O.K. Let's go.'

We lifted the wardrobe, myself at the top, Sam at the foot, and off we trudged, reached Newhaven, put the wardrobe down into the water at the seashore and jumped in. Started off, holding the door open so that we could see where we were going, paddling with our hands. We were soon well away from the shore. Both of us had enormous hands. In fact, the size of our hands was responsible for our deep friendship. They measured exactly a metre – just over a yard – from heel to fingertip. This can be a handicap. Some coarse people jeered. We had to pay extra for bespoke clothes as the tailor used large quantities of fine sailcloth on the pockets. A famous abstract painter, whom I shall not name, once painted my jacket and trousers, inside-out, because the pockets made such an 'exciting composition'. These are his very words; 'exciting composition'.

Anyway, Sam and I were paddling along in the water; we were hitting seventeen knots – twenty knots with the wind behind us. This was a double wardrobe, a door between two spaces, and, of course, we had brought a lot of coat-hooks in case the weather became stormy and sandwiches. Then – terrible, terrible – it started fogging.

'Ten knots, Sam.'

'Ten knots it is, Jim.'

We feathered our hands to reduce speed.

'VO VO – VO VO VO!'

We skidded to a standstill, terror striking at our stomachs and hearts, peering through the thick. A great craft loomed at us and crash! It splintered the wardrobe into many pieces. Sam and I were flung overboard, one on either side of the liner, for it was a liner, and we drifted helplessly until the boat passed us, tossed in its wake. Luckily we were not damaged by its propellers.

'Hello, Sam!' I boomed.

'Hello, Jim!' Sam boomed.

Thanks to our cupped hands, our voices carried well. We swam towards one another, met, and shook hands, with gratitude, in ourselves, for being alive.

'How can we reach shore?'

'Easy,' said Sam, 'watch this,' then clasped his hands and sat on them.

'By gad,' I cried, and clasped my hands and sat on them. We were unable to move at any speed, as there was nothing with which we could propel ourselves. And we couldn't sit on one hand and paddle with the other, that would just have been damn silly. So we sat.

The fog lifted. We found ourselves close to the shore, so close indeed that we waded to dry land, then walked inland, passing some sand-dunes, on to the road where we observed a man in a black suit bearing down on us. Sam raised a hand in greeting.

'Hello,' he smiled.

The stranger raised his hand. We turned to one another in stupefaction. His hand measured exactly a metre from heel to fingertip.

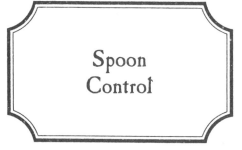

'Hello! – Hello, Spoon Control?'

'Spoon Control speaking.'

'I should like to report that one of my spoons has gone out of control.'

'Mhm! What kind of spoon?'

'A silver teaspoon.'

'Yes – well, just tell me what happened.'

'It was only five minutes ago. I was spooning sugar into my tea, and I had just spooned the third spoon in, when it suddenly jumped out of the cup, ran across the table on to the floor and out of the house. We know it's somewhere in the garden, but it's not showing itself.'

'That's interesting. This is the third case we've had today of a silver teaspoon out of control. What distinguishing marks are there on it?'

'Well, there is the heel-mark, of course, and my monogram.'

'Monogram? Your initials?'

'Mhm.'

'What are they?'

'A B C D E F G H I J K L M N O P Q R S T U V W X Y.'

'And you have *all* these initials on your teaspoon?'

'Yes.'

'And you wonder why your teaspoon has gone out of control?'

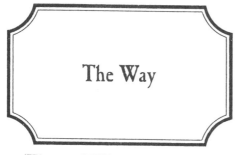

The Way

One evening at eight o'clock, I was standing outside my hotel in the pouring rain, when the old man approached me.

'Can you tell me the way?' he whispered.

'The way? Which way? The way to where?'

'Just can you tell me the way?' he said, with a hint of irritation in his voice.

There was a pathetic ring to the words, and I, perhaps indiscreetly, said, 'Come along with me.' We walked down the street, crossed at the zebra crossing, turned back up the street till we were opposite the hotel, and crossed once more.

'Here we are,' I said, 'here is the way.'

We were back where we started from. The old man glared up at me. His eyes had a puzzled look in them. They seemed to say, 'I have been here before.' His hands clenched and unclenched.

'Look,' he said querulously, 'can you tell me the way?'

I looked into his eyes, and of course I should have said 'No! I don't know the way,' but I felt I would try again. We walked down the street, turned left at the corner, worked our way round the block till we were back to the hotel entrance. Tears began to spurt from the old man's eyes, but at the same time a red fire of anger gleamed in them. His fist lunged at me, and hit me on the breast: a feeble blow, but strong enough to show that this was not a casual inquiry. This time I took him *up* the street. We walked a long way till we came to the park. The park gates were just closing and we were barely able to slip inside and hide in the bushes till the keeper had gone. Then we walked on to the path and strode confidently, though soaking, to the top of the hill.

'Right,' I said, 'now watch! and I will show you the way!!'

I flapped my arms wildly by my sides, up and down, up and down. My eyes half-closed, my arms flapping wildly, my knees bent slightly; I took off, as I usually do at this time of night.

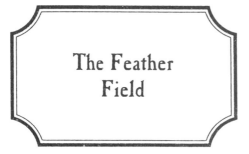

The Feather Field

'I say, Stopbarrow, stop the car, will you.'

'Certainly, sir.'

'I want to look at this great field of feathers. What a grand sight, glinting in the morning sun, white and gold. I'm going to get out and have a look at them.'

'They're very fine, sir.'

'Look! There's the farmer's house. Drive over and I'll have a word with him. – Stop the car. There's a notice. "Please do not ask me any silly questions or I shall chase you off my land." Mm! Sounds a recalcitrant sort of fellow. Let's go along. We shan't ask him any silly questions. – Good afternoon!'

'Good afternoon!'

'We were just admiring your feather field.'

'Glad you like it.'

'Do you find a good market for them?'

'Oh, yes. Yes. Sell a lot to milliners. Best stuff of course. Some to the theatrical trade and the poor quality feathers to pillow manufacturers for their pillows.'

'I see. It must be quite remunerative, then.'

'Remunerative? What does that mean?'

'You know. Make a lot of money out of it.'

'Don't go poking your nose too far, mister!'

'Oh. Very well. How do you manage to – '

'Now, be careful!'

'How do you manage to grow feathers so tall? They must be seven or eight feet.'

'Well, they're not seven or eight feet. They're only six or seven feet. I grow them from seed.'

'From seed?'

'Yes. That's what I said. I grow them from seed.'

'But – they're birds' feathers, aren't they?'

'Yes.'

'What kind of seed do you grow them from?'

'Now I warned you. You read the notice down there, didn't you?'

'Well –'

'Well! Well what? You want to know what kind of seed they are. Don't you? Eh? They all ask me this question. Go on! Gerrout! Gerrout! Where's my cudgel? Get off my fields. Get out of my house. I don't want to answer that question!'

'Please tell me. Please don't hit me! Please don't hit me! Just tell me what kind of seed you grow them from!'

'Gerrout! I hate that question. Drives me crazy! I lie awake sleeping at night because of it. Gerraway! Gerrout! Take that!'

'Ff! Ooh! What kind of seed?'

'And that!'

'Oh! What kind of seed? I want to know. Aha! I want to know! What kind of seed?'

'Bird seed! Now get out!'

Cold Potato

I was walking along the street, in the heat, at noontide, calling, 'Cold potato! Cold potato!' You see, I sell cold potatoes in the heat and I sell hot potatoes in the wintertime, when it's cold. In this way, I can keep working all the year round. So I was calling 'Cold potato! Cold potato!' and the street was absolutely empty, and it was burning hot and I was hoping that the potatoes would stay cold. I didn't used to carry many potatoes with me. I'd have – say – three or four potatoes in each pocket embedded in ice-chips, with a sponge to catch the drips, and people who wanted a cold potato would throw me down $1.40, and I would throw them up a cold potato. People round this part like cold potatoes and I can't blame them; the heat they have here, cold potatoes are very welcome.

Suddenly, a window opens, it must have been a twelfth-storey flat, and a woman's head shouts out, 'Hey, down there! Cold potato man! I want a cold potato!'

I thought, 'A twelve-storey fling.' However, I shouted down, 'Right you are! They're $1.40,' and she threw down $1.40 – and I threw up a cold potato. Well, it didn't get further than the third storey, and it came back down. The next time I threw it, it reached the fifth storey. Then the eighth, and in the end it reached her storey. By this time every window in the street was filled with a grinning head.

She grabs hold of the potato and she feels it: I can see her feeling it in her hands. And she shouts down, 'Hey! This potato isn't cold. It's lukewarm.'

'Well,' I shout up, 'who told you to live on the twelfth storey? Naturally it's lukewarm. Look at all the time I've spent trying to throw it up to you.'

'Here,' she shouts, 'take your lukewarm potato! I want my money back.' And she lets the potato drop. I caught it deftly and put it back in my pocket to chill. With everybody watching and all the heads grinning, I knew I had to

return her money. So I threw up her $1.40. It reached her first time.

'Hey, cold potato man,' she yells, 'this $1.40's lukewarm!' Everybody applauded. I dragged all the potatoes out of my pockets and threw them into the road. Then I jumped up and down on them for a while till I recovered my good spirits.

The Secret

'Hello! Agent 9?'
'Yes.'
'The prisoner won't talk.'
'O – ho! Torture him!'
'No good. Nil response.'
'Brainwash him!'

'No good. Nil response. Doesn't appear to possess a brain.'

'There must be a new way. Yes. I have an idea. Design a meal for him!'

'A meal? Would it worm the secret from him?'

'Not an ordinary meal. A meal composed of unusual objects. Just imagine – he enters the room, make it a long room, and a long table – one chair, right at the far end, and all sorts of unusual foods on it. By the time he'd reached the chair, he'd be ready to talk.'

'Fine! But if he saw all the foods at once, it might not have the desired effect. I suggest we use sandwiches.'

'M – hm! A great plate of sandwiches, and put them in a broad room, on a broad plate. Have it ready in thirty minutes.'

'Right!'

'Here you are, prisoner. Through this door.'
'Ah! A broad room?'
'Yes! A broad room! Sit on that chair.'
'All right. What do I do now?'

.68. 'What do you see before you?'

'A plate of sandwiches.'

'Go ahead. Have a sandwich!'

'Can I examine the sandwich? Maybe you are going to poison me. Maybe you don't want my secret any more.'

'Go ahead, examine it if you wish.'

'Hmhm! This sandwich contains a shoe. Must I eat it?'

'Only if you wish. Try another sandwich.'

'Hm! A first-class ticket to Y'Hup. I shan't eat that. Do you mind if I look at the rest of the sandwiches? I must confess I'm fascinated.'

'No. Go ahead!'

'A 6B pencil. Mm! Soft eating! A gramophone with a handle! You're doing this on a shoe-string! A stuffed advocado! A toffee cuirass!! – I'll tell you my secret! I'll tell you my secret!'

'All right. Tell me your secret.'

'Spiz dronk.'

'What?'

'Spiz dronk! That's my secret.'

'Spiz dronk! What the hell's that?'

'I don't know. When we got our orders, we were only given a little bit of the secret, each. My bit is "spiz dronk".'

The Competition

'Let's have a competition,' said Jean.

'That's a good idea,' I said. We needed money badly. The rent had not been paid for thirty-one years and the landlord was becoming restive. I was uncomfortable when I passed him.

'What kind of a competition?'

'A coughing competition.'

'You're mad,' I sneered. 'A coughing competition!'

'Take it or leave it,' she snarled.

'I'll take it,' I quavered. Who would cross Jean? 'What'll we do?'

'Firstly,' she said smugly, consulting a purple notebook, 'we insert an advertisement in one of those . . . er . . . boards outside newsagents' windows, and advertise it. Eh – something like – "There will be a coughing competition, held at so-and-so on the so-and-so, eh bring so-and-so money for your entrance fee. First prize will be eh – say – so-and-so, and other complimentary prizes, like – eh – cough pastilles." You know the sort of thing.'

'That's a good idea,' I said. 'Will you write out the notice; you seem to have it pretty well.'

'Yes,' she replied, 'eh, have you a postcard?'

I went to my drawer and found a piece of cardboard. We painted it white, then wrote on it. Jean took it the following morning to the newsagent. He stuck it up. We had 78 replies, 74 of which enclosed the entrance money, which was one and ninepence, a good round sum.

'Fine!' said Jean, 'now all we need do is to find the right sort of place: 78 people: we could almost do it in the house.'

So we wrote the competitors, giving them our address, telling them to come on the following evening at 8.15 in order to give the children a chance to get to sleep. Then we got an orange box from the plumber and placed a little piece of flowered cretonne on top and down the front – and placed it before the

open window. Next day; competition day; everything was ready. A three four
pound note and several boxes, large to small, of cough drops, cough gums,
cough cure. Then we waited. 8.15! Not a soul arrived. By nine I was pacing the
floor and at ten Jean burst into tears.

'Where were they? Where were they?'

We did not despair completely because we had the three four pound note,
but it seemed most peculiar. Jean sobbed and sobbed.

'Look, darling,' I said. 'Just sit there, will you?' pointing to a spot right in
front of the cretonne box, I mean the orange box with the cretonne curtain
thing on it, then I stood on top of the box and started to cough, something
like this: (*coughing*). Jean started to cheer up and after about twenty-five
minutes of steady coughing, her tears were completely gone and she was full
of smiles. We paid our arrears of rent with the competition money. We just
have these – cough pastilles and sweets and bottles.

The Embarrassed Handywoman

'Are you the blind date I'm supposed to meet here?'

'I expect I am.'

'Stand with your back to the wall, and let me look at you. – Fine! Now turn round! – Splendid. Come on. We'll go for a walk.'

'Oh, thank you! Thank you!'

'What's your name?'

'My name is Anna.'

'Anna. A pretty name. My name's Adam.'

'Anna and Adam. Hm!' (*Laughs.*)

'You're a personable girl. How does it come that nobody's taken you out before?'

'Please don't talk about it.'

'Is there something wrong with you?'

'Just please don't talk about it.'

'Your clothes are fine, but why are you wearing that T-shaped glove?'

'Please – please don't talk about that. Please let's talk about something else. Aren't the trees lovely here!'

'There aren't any trees.'

'Well – isn't it a nice day!'

'It's freezing!'

'Oh, well, you talk about something.'

'All right, eh – I don't know what to talk about, you've driven all the thoughts out of my head. Let me take your hand.'

'Oh, no, please don't take my hand!'

'Come on, no one's going to hurt you. – Goodness gracious! Here, take your glove off. What's this?'

'It's a brush.'

'Why are you holding a brush?'

'I'm not holding a brush. It's me.'

'Let me see. – Goodness' sake. Why – I'm sorry. Here. Here. Here's your glove. – Why is your hand a brush?'

'Now you know why people don't go out with me. My hand's a brush because I'm very easily embarrassed, and whenever I'm embarrassed my hand turns into a brush.'

'That's handy.'

'It is indeed, because whenever I want to do any brushwork around the house, I just embarrass myself.'

'Hahahahahahaha! I say. That's jolly good. Can you embarrass yourself easily?'

'Oh, not really. It's very difficult but I have a friend who comes over and embarrasses me, and then – '

'A girl friend?'

'Naturally.'

'And is she good at embarrassing you?'

'Yes. She can be a trifle vulgar, but she manages, if we need the brush, you see.'

'Can it do any kind of brushwork?'

'Oh yes. We can paint the walls with it – brush our clothes and you don't need to clean it or anything like that because all you need do is stop being embarrassed and it changes back to a hand.'

'Oh, that's fun.'

'And as I've said before, it's handy too.'

'Brush my coat, will you!'

'All right.'

'I say, it is good – oh!'

'I'm sorry, my brush is a hand again. I'm not embarrassed any more with you.'

'That's nice.'

'Adam! I do like you!'

'That's v – Hey! Anna, look at my hand. It's turning into a dustpan. I think that you and I are meant for one another.'

The Bespoke Chicken

'Hello! What are you doing there?'

'Weaving.'

'Weaving? Weaving what?'

'I'm weaving a chicken.'

'Oh! You've got one of those, have you?'

'Mmm! Look! It's finished! Do you like it?'

'Gosh. It looks lovely. Are you going to cook it right away?'

'Oh no. You have to hang it for a few days, and then it'll be ready.'

'Eh, do they taste – as good as the real thing?'

'Mm! They taste *better*, and they work out much cheaper too, making them yourself.'

'*I* must try that.'

'Of course, the capital outlet's a bit on the heavy side: £200 for the loom.'

'£200! You're going to have to weave a lot of chickens.'

'I know, but I don't eat them all myself. I sell most of them to friends and neighbours. They come back for more – find them delicious.'

'That's jolly interesting. Can you weave anything else besides chickens?'

'Oh, yes. You can weave any kind of animal you like, provided, of course, that you can get the, you know, the correct weave for it. The shop stocks mostly chicken weave, or you could buy a dog weave, or cat weave or elephant weave, though, aha, there's not much call for elephant weave, not in this country anyway. Possibly in India, but I think chicken weave is the most popular.'

'Dog weave! – I shouldn't mind having a woven dog. I presume I could use my own design.'

'Oh, yes. You design it yourself and then just pop it into the loom. You weave and out comes the dog, just the way you want it.'

'What do I do about the dog making suitable animal noises?'

'Lead it to a tree, then tear of a bit of the outer covering.'

Do You Ever
Feel Lonely

The New Nose

'Do you sell noses?'

'Of course, we sell noses. Can't you read the legend on the window: "P. Gonk, nose-monger"?'

'I'm sorry, sir. I can't read.'

'Oh! Sorry, sorry. What brought you in?'

'I saw your nose at the window.'

'Ah-hah! Now what sort of nose do you want?'

'I do the shopping in my household. My wife is always holding up to me a friend of hers, needless to say, not of mine, who, she says, has a good nose for a bargain.'

'Yes.'

'Do you stock noses for a bargain?'

'Hmm. Yes. Yes. I believe I could find something for you. Now, do you want a nose like your own, or do you want a different shape?'

'I think I should like a new shape. Do the noses – are they retractable?'

'Ah! Now retractable is a lot more expensive. You see, most noses normally don't retract, and if you want to have a retractable nose, and your own nose: if you want a retractable one you'll require your own nose too, then, you have to pay through the nose. And I don't know, begging your pardon, I don't know whether you could afford such a nose.'

'How much would such a nose cost?'

'That, again, is a little difficult to say, as the prices vary tremendously within the retractable nose range. Naturally, the greater the surface area, the greater the price, adenoids inclusive.'

'Yes.'

'I'll tell you. We'll try one or two on, then discuss the price. Will you sit down here before the green curtain. That's right. No no. In front of the curtain. Facing it. Closer. Now place your nose through the hole in the c – that's right. Now. Hold it! This might hurt a trifle.' 'Ow!!' 'Sorry! Just keep

still. That's right. Shan't be a second. Right! Now, look at yourself in the
mirror.' (*Prolonged laughing.*)

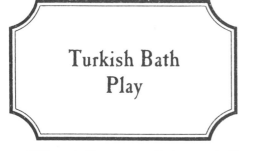

Turkish Bath
Play

'Good afternoon.'

'Good afternoon.'

'I should like to perform a play here in your Turkish bath.'

'A play in the Turkish bath? You can't do that. There are all these people here.'

'What difference will that make?'

'Well, they're wearing nothing except Turkish towels.'

'Oh! That won't worry me.'

'It'll worry them.'

'I don't think so. You see, this play is about a Turkish bath.'

'Ah, I see. And you want to use the Turkish bath as a setting for your Turkish bath play, I presume, because it's about a Turkish bath. Is that right?'

'That's right. You have it.'

'Well, that sounds reasonable. Will you want to do any rehearsing?'

'No no! We'll just come and perform the play.'

'I see. All right. How about an audience?'

'Oh no. I don't want an audience.'

'Well, what are you going to do about all those people who are in the Turkish bath having a Turkish bath?'

'Oh. That's all right for them. They'll be perfectly welcome to hang around and watch, but the play's not primarily intended for them and we certainly don't want an audience coming in. It would just be ridiculous, wouldn't it?'

'Yes. Of course. Of course it would be ridiculous.'

'Would you tell me what your play's about?'

'Oh, I don't think I could tell you what the play's about.'

'Why not? Is there something wrong with it?'

'No no, I don't think I'd like to tell you what it's about. I'd just like to do

my Turkish play here, in the Turkish bath, and then go away again.'

'Is your play all right? I don't want you to do your play in the Turkish bath and then have a lot of trouble: newspapers or court injunctions or whatever happens.'

'You needn't worry about that. This play's perfectly all right.'

'Now, what time do you want to do this play at?'

'Oh. Any time would suit me.'

'Well, any time would suit me.'

'Do you think morning, or afternoon or evening?'

'I think morning would be a good time. At what time do you open?'

'9 o'clock.'

'9 o'clock. That would be quite a good time.'

'You mean, start at 9 o'clock?'

'Oh no, I shouldn't want to start right away. Could I start at – about 2 minutes past 9?'

'Yes. I think you could. How long does your play last?'

'It lasts four minutes.'

'Well, that should take you through to em–9.2 – eh – 9.6 – 6 minutes past 9.'

'I'm not exactly sure of the timing, but it's pretty roughly four minutes.'

'How many members have you in the cast?'

'There's just me.'

'You mean you're going to do a play with just yourself?'

'Yes.'

'But you said – but you said earlier on – that – *we* were going to do a play.'

'Oh yes. Of course. I play all the parts. There are 114 parts and I play them all. Oh, I suppose I may as well tell you what the play's about. It's about 113 people who are trying to lose weight.'

'Ah. And what about the 114th person?'

'He massages the other 113 people.'

'And do they *lose* weight?'

'In four minutes?'

The Curse

'Is this the Friendless Society?'

'Yes. This is the Friendless Society. You want to join?'

'I want to join the Friendless Society.'

'Phewph! What a horrible smell. Is it coming from you? It smells like the kitchen sink.'

'Yes. It's me. I smell like the kitchen sink.'

'Tough luck. It's an awful smell. How did you come by it?'

'Well, it happened when I was eleven. When I was eleven, I was sitting in the garden. I was a horrible boy in those days, you know. My head full of guns and soldiers and fighting. Well, I'm sitting in the garden and this fairy comes along and perches on my knee, and she looks at me and she says: "Do you like me, little boy?" And this sickened me to my soul. Could you imagine what would have happened if one of my pals came along and this fairy saying "Do you like me, little boy?" – so I caught her a swipe right in the middle and knocked her flat on her back on the grass. And she got up, and she was furious of course, and she came flying right up to my face and she shouts: "I'm going to put a curse on you. You're going to smell like the kitchen sink till the day you die." Then she flew away before I could take another swipe at her.'

'So you've got to go around the world like this till the day you die?'

'Yes. I'm used to it now, myself.'

'Well, I'm not. I'm afraid you can't come in here. The members are friendless, but they're not as friendless as that.'

'Well, what am I going to do?'

'Why not start another branch. Call it "Friendless Society Branch One." Let people join who are afflicted with impaired olfactory organs.'

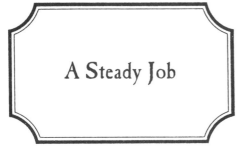

A Steady Job

'Hello, Sam!'

'Hello, Daddy. You back?'

'Yes, son. What in the – where's your mother?'

'She's in the house, somewhere.'

'Doris! Doris, what the hell's Sam doing out in the garden buried up to his ankles?'

'Oh, Bill. I'm *so* glad you're home, dear. Three weeks is a long time.'

'Yes, darling. What's Sam doing out in the garden?'

'Bill, I'm broken-hearted. Oh, I'm so glad you're home. Bill! I don't know where to begin. The day after you went, some kid at school told Sam he was small. You know how sensitive Sam is. He came home, dug a couple of little holes in the garden, stuck his feet in, stamped the earth down and poured some water over himself and stood there – all night; I didn't find out till the next morning and I said, "What are you doing, Sam?" and he said, "I'm trying to grow," and he told me about this fellow at school. I tried to dissuade him but you know Sam. Well, at the end of the week I thought I'd had enough. Despite all his protests, I tried to dig him out – and I couldn't.'

'What do you mean, dear?'

'He'd taken root.'

'Taken root! You're mad!'

'No, I'm not. His toes have started to grow and have worked their way down into the earth.'

'You mean you can't – get him out? Surely you can find which way his toes have gone and ease them out.'

'Oh, you don't understand, Bill. Bill, they've – grown all in different directions.'

'Yes, but it's not an impossible job.'

'Bill, Sam is going to have to stay there for ever. Two of his toes have gone under the electric railway at the bottom of the garden and are up in a garden on

the other side – lucky it's someone we know. We'll never be able to get him out. I spoke to the railway company. They refuse to allow tunnelling underneath their line. They were pretty mad with his toes growing under the line as it is.'

'Do you mean that Sam is there for ever?'

'Yes. Yes, Bill. I foolishly let Sam know about this, and he was as pleased as punch; you see – he's very happy there – growing – in the garden.'

'But we can't have that.'

'Oh, Bill, you know you said that you would let Sam do whatever he wanted to. He's old enough now to know his own mind. He wants to stand in the garden and grow. I think we ought to let him. Don't you?'

'All right then, Doris.'

'Bill. Go and tell Sam that it's all right. He's worried about you.'

'O.K., Doris, I'll tell him. (*Loud*) Sam! It's all right!'

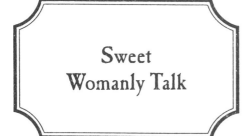

Sweet
Womanly Talk

When I was a youth and in my 'ivory pedestal' period, I longed to hear two women talking together. I longed to hear the sweet womanly things they would say to one another. So one day I tiptoed after my sister Winifred and her friend Persephone as they left the dining-room for Winifred's bedroom. They were both nineteen. I stationed myself at the keyhole to listen to what sweet, womanly talk would issue from their maidenly lips: and this is what I heard:

'Oh, Persephone darling, what a beautiful wonderful day it has been.'

'Yes, darling Winifred, indeed it has. When I meandered along the path to your house today, and saw the tulips blazing in bloom, my bosom nigh burst with the excess of ecstasy engendered. The gentle warmth creeping from the grass; the azure sky above; *all* combined to create in me a feeling of –spiritous well-being.'

'Oh, Persephone, how well you express yourself. I have been confined to

the house this morning, but I took out my opal ring, gazed into its fiery
depths. There was a misting cloudiness, and I fell a-dreaming, and dreamed of
a knight in tall armour, coming to march to take me away to a sweet, cloudy
land, where all would be calm and peaceful.'

Outside the door, I writhed with pleasure. 'This is real, woman's talk,' I
thought. 'My God! How beautifully they speak to one another. What pure,
decent, innocent thoughts.' And I left them, surfeited with the rich language.
Had I stayed longer, I should have heard:

'Has your brother gone, 'fred?'

'Yes, he's gone, Perse.'

'Dig that crazy brother of yours, 'fred. Him and his ivory pedestals. He
drives me up the wall.'

'Me too. Someone ought to tell him. Perse, why don't you give him some
of that —you know?'

'Do you think . . .?'

'Of course! Oh, Ivor, dear brother, my friend Persephone wishes to see you
for a trice!'

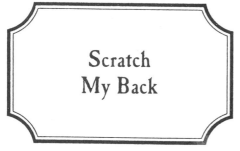

Scratch My Back

'Scratch my back, mister!'

This from an old man of eighty-two, wearing a greasy, old, faded, pink overcoat. I shrank from his coat with distaste.

'Look, sir, I've just gone and cut my nails.'

'Ah!' he said, 'I'm in agony.'

I thought, 'Poor man!' 'Tell you what,' I said, 'if you care to wait till my nails grow, I'll give you a good scratch.'

'Oh!' he said, 'how long does it take for your nails to grow? Ff! I'm in agony.'

'Well, maybe a week,' I said.

'A week!' And he looked around despairingly, but there was no one else there. 'All right,' he said. So we sat down – and watched my nails growing.

Every day, every now and again, he would look down at his own nails, which were long and filthy and cracked, and try to work them round to his back, but of course he couldn't get them near the itchy places.

The first couple of days, we talked pleasantly together – small talk – the weather. The weather was the big topic. You see, we were sitting on the kerb with our feet in the gutter – and it was pouring. But we knew that as long as we stayed where we were, the stone on which we were sitting would remain dry, albeit cold.

On the fifth day, I became restless. From the condition of my nails, I knew that in a couple of days I'd have to scratch this woman's back. 'Look here,' I said, 'why don't you rub your back against the wall?' She looked at me, hurt. She'd been looking forward for five days to a good scratch, and here was I trying to pan her off on a wall.

'No,' she whispered, trying to keep her temper as well as she could, 'it wouldn't get between my blade-bones.' I submitted to her logic.

Sixth day came. It had been raining steadily all these six days. I hadn't slept
very much. – I didn't feel like sleeping much anyway with the rain pouring
down on me. – We were both quite wet, but you know, when you sit out in the
rain for six days, it doesn't seem to matter any more about it raining. And I
felt myself becoming very calm and thoughtful, and I think the woman did too.
The seventh day dawned, and as soon as it was light enough, I looked at my
nails. They were long – they were sharp. I turned to the woman – I felt like a
martyr – a bit smug and noble – 'O.K.,' I said, 'present your back.' She looked
full at me. I couldn't read her face. The writing was illegible.

'My back's stopped itching. Thanks all the same.' She stretched luxuriously
into her mustard twin-suit and staggered away into the dawn. I looked after her
in honest admiration. What a stoic! But what is this! She turns, and with a
look of agony, staggers back. Quick as thought, I pull out my scissors and cut
my nails.

The
Impresario

I am an impresario. A man came in and said, 'I can hit a hundred women.'

I ran out and fetched in the first hundred women I could put my fingers on. He hit them all without moving a muscle.

'This is marvellous!' I shouted. 'I'll put you in tonight's show. How much?'
'I'll do it for the love of it,' he replied.

'No, I must offer you a retainer in case the talent scouts grab you,' I said.
'All right. A hundred nicker,' he said.

That night I sat out front to watch – a thing I hadn't done since Prunella Hay – probably for the vicarious experience. Dressed in Naples yellow dungarees with a silver hankie, he came on and said, 'I want a hundred bigoted shrews married to long-suffering husbands.' A great horde of glittering sequined ladies rose like a cloud of dust and made for the stage. He peeled off the first hundred. 'Go and sit down the rest of you. I'll probably need you for an encore,' he said.

It was wonderful to watch him at work. He would bring back his open hand and swing it round. *Smack! Slap!* And the woman would stagger down, shaking with anger, to sit fuming in her seat. Everyone was loving it, and when he finished his tally there was a tremendous gust of applause and great deep baying shouts of 'Encore! Encore!'

He bowed, snapped his fingers, and another hundred women ran up to be slapped. *Slap! Slap slap!* He slapped them silly and sent them back.

When every woman in the theatre had been slapped, he shouted, 'Hey you!' to a frail, mousy woman with gold-rimmed spectacles, 'you haven't been slapped.'

She rose, lifting her chair with her, and brought it on to the stage. Then she climbed on to the chair, worked her way up his shoulders till she stood on top of his head and called in a strident contralto, 'Cockadoodledoo!'

The curtain dropped and I raced round and offered him a thirty-two-year contract.

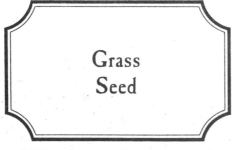

Grass
Seed

'Hello, son.'

'Hello, Daddy, can I do an experiment with you?'

'What sort of an experiment, son?'

'Daddy. Can I plant grass seed on your bald head?'

'All right, son. Let me see it.'

'Here you are, Daddy.'

'This is not lawn grass seed, is it?'

'No, Daddy. It's a special kind I bought in a shop. It's very quick-growing. Will you sit in the armchair and then I can reach your head?'

'O.K.'

'Do you mind if I press the nutmeg grater on to your scalp, to make little holes for the grass to seed in?'

'No. Not at all, son. Just press it gently. Ffff! Hey, take it easy! Ah! Take it easy, son. Here! Here! Here!'

'Finished! Some seed – a little water – there. Here's a mirror. Watch!'

'Hey, son, it's beginning to sprout.'

'Gosh, Daddy, so it is. Look how quickly it's growing! It's three inches long already, in four minutes. Aw. It's marvellous. You can actually see it growing. What does it feel like, Daddy?'

'Oh! It's sharp, and very fine too: almost like hair but a lot harder, more of a bristle. I say, I do have a fine head of hair. Son! Go and fetch me the scissors, will you! Thanks. Now cut off all the rest of my hair. I'm going to have all my hair grass.'

'Oh, Daddy, don't bother.'

'Yes, yes, son!'

'Oh, Daddy, it was only an experiment I was doing on you.'

'What do you mean? You mean you didn't buy the grass seed specially for me?'

'Oh no, Daddy. I wanted it for myself.'

.94.   'For yourself? What are you going to do with it?'

'Well, when I go to bed tonight, I'll take all my clothes off and I'll squeeze the nutmeg grater all over myself. All over my body and my arms and my legs and my head, then I'm going to rub the grass seed in and water it. We're having "Old Shivery" for English tomorrow, and you know how nervous *she* is!'